Success
Assessment Papers

More Verbal Reasoning

age 10–11

Colin Sowter

Sample page

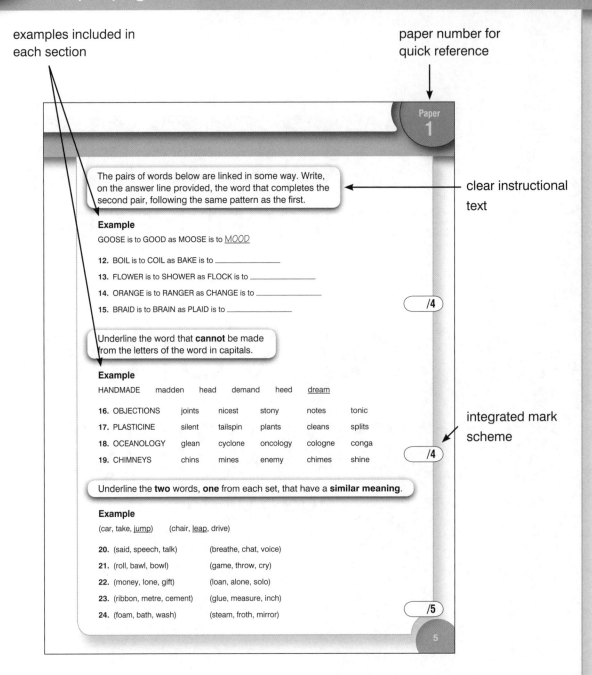

Paper
1

The pairs of words below are linked in some way. Write, on the answer line provided, the word that completes the second pair, following the same pattern as the first.

clear instructional text

Example

GOOSE is to GOOD as MOOSE is to <u>MOOD</u>

12. BOIL is to COIL as BAKE is to _____

13. FLOWER is to SHOWER as FLOCK is to _____

14. ORANGE is to RANGER as CHANGE is to _____

15. BRAID is to BRAIN as PLAID is to _____

/4

Underline the word that **cannot** be made from the letters of the word in capitals.

Example

HANDMADE   madden   head   demand   heed   <u>dream</u>

16. OBJECTIONS	joints	nicest	stony	notes	tonic
17. PLASTICINE	silent	tailspin	plants	cleans	splits
18. OCEANOLOGY	glean	cyclone	oncology	cologne	conga
19. CHIMNEYS	chins	mines	enemy	chimes	shine

/4

integrated mark scheme

Underline the **two** words, **one** from each set, that have a **similar meaning**.

Example

(car, take, <u>jump</u>)   (chair, <u>leap</u>, drive)

20. (said, speech, talk)   (breathe, chat, voice)

21. (roll, bawl, bowl)   (game, throw, cry)

22. (money, lone, gift)   (loan, alone, solo)

23. (ribbon, metre, cement)   (glue, measure, inch)

24. (foam, bath, wash)   (steam, froth, mirror)

/5

5

Contents

PAPER 1

In the following sentences, a word of **four letters** is hidden across the **end** of one word and the **start** of the next word. Write the hidden word on the line provided. The letter order **cannot** be changed.

Example

The shop was la**st op**en on Tuesday. <u>stop</u>

1. I don't think that bath uses up much water. _____

2. How would you describe stairs to a Martian? _____

3. He went online straightaway after getting home. _____

4. Don't drag everyone down with you! _____

5. He was a year younger than his sister. _____

6. They went to the skating rink this morning. _____

/6

Move **one** letter from the first word and add it to the second word to make two new words. Do **not** rearrange any other letters. Write **both** new words, which **must make sense**, on the lines provided.

Example

table   reed   →   <u>tale</u>   <u>breed</u>

7. tripe   hat   →   _____   _____

8. gear   kin   →   _____   _____

9. blown   one   →   _____   _____

10. bless   vie   →   _____   _____

11. caned   ream   →   _____   _____

/5

The pairs of words below are linked in some way. Write, on the answer line provided, the word that completes the second pair, following the same pattern as the first.

Example

GOOSE is to GOOD as MOOSE is to <u>MOOD</u>

12. BOIL is to COIL as BAKE is to _____

13. FLOWER is to SHOWER as FLOCK is to _____

14. ORANGE is to RANGER as CHANGE is to _____

15. BRAID is to BRAIN as PLAID is to _____

/4

Underline the word that **cannot** be made from the letters of the word in capitals.

Example

HANDMADE   madden   head   demand   heed   <u>dream</u>

16. OBJECTIONS   joints   nicest   stony   notes   tonic

17. PLASTICINE   silent   tailspin   plants   cleans   splits

18. OCEANOLOGY   glean   cyclone   oncology   cologne   conga

19. CHIMNEYS   chins   mines   enemy   chimes   shine

/4

Underline the **two** words, **one** from each set, that have a **similar meaning**.

Example

(car, take, <u>jump</u>)   (chair, <u>leap</u>, drive)

20. (said, speech, talk)   (breathe, chat, voice)

21. (roll, bawl, bowl)   (game, throw, cry)

22. (money, lone, gift)   (loan, alone, solo)

23. (ribbon, metre, cement)   (glue, measure, inch)

24. (foam, bath, wash)   (steam, froth, mirror)

/5

The word in capitals has had a group of three letters taken out. These **three** letters spell another word, without rearranging the order. Write the **three-letter** word on the line provided. The sentence needs to make sense.

Example

I like my bacon cooked very CRI   _SPY_

25. In our HROOM we have a lovely new basin.   _____

26. She made sure the potatoes were well SCBED.   _____

27. His flat could do with a new PET.   _____

28. I prefer a plain TERN.   _____

29. Don't get too close to the gas, it may IGE!   _____

/5

Underline the **two** words in each line that are **different** from the others.

Example

<u>potato</u>   lemon   banana   <u>cabbage</u>   strawberry

30. jolly   happy   grumpy   cheerful   sad

31. blaring   rowdy   faint   hushed   muffled

32. savoury   salty   soft   bitter   crunchy

33. rhubarb   orange   greens   spinach   lemon

34. prove   establish   confirm   brake   came

/5

Underline the **two** words, **one** from each set, that when put together, make one new, correctly spelt word. The order of the letters does not change. **The word from the group on the left always comes first.**

Example

(run, <u>use</u>, give)   (take, <u>less</u>, red)

35. (cap, need, man)   (ace, able, us)

36. (fast, man, run)   (less, old, age)

37. (clasp, clam, dam)   (ping, less, hole)

38. (haul, wheel, float)   (ace, age, wing)

39. (damp, canal, dam)   (less, water, age)

/5

Underline **one** word from the list in brackets that goes equally well with both pairs of words outside the brackets.

Example

(ribbon, <u>present</u>, play, theatre, party)

gift, token   show, demonstrate

40. (mend, knit, machine, anger, needle)

sewing, cotton   annoy, aggravate

41. (trees, leaves, dunes, earth, roots)

branches, twigs   deserts, abandons

42. (stuff, dislike, object, property, decry)

thing, possession   disapprove, denounce

43. (trade, shop, purchase, refund, receipt)

business, customers   swap, exchange

/4

In the first set of three words, the middle word has been made from letters in the other two words. Complete the second set of words in the **same** way, to make the missing word, **which must make sense**. Write your answers on the lines provided.

Example

fast (tea) real   leaf (<u>fir</u>) hire

44. pram (ape) type   kick (_____) chat

45. warm (raps) spun   tank (_____) lisp

46. nail (line) ones   nits (_____) pare

47. lean (real) near   died (_____) diet

48. east (fees) face   coke (_____) dune

/5

Letters stand for numbers. Work out the answer to each sum. Write your answer as a **letter** on the line provided.

Example

If A = 2, B = 3, C = 4, D = 5, E = 6, F = 8, what is the answer to this sum written as a letter:

D + B = <u>F</u>

If A = 2, B = 3, C = 4, D = 5, E = 6, what is:

49. E – A = _____

50. B + D – C = _____

51. D – A = _____

52. E – D + B = _____

53. E + B – C = _____

/5

Write the numbers that complete each sequence in the most sensible way.

Example

<u>12</u>   <u>14</u>   16   18   20   22

54. _____   _____   7   10   13   16

55. _____   11   14   _____   20

56. 19   _____   _____   58   71   84

57. 2   11   _____   56   _____   137

58. 7   19   9   21   _____   _____

/5

59. Adam, Ben, Clare, Donna and Evan are all avid fans of their local football team.
Ben, Donna and Evan have the home kit.
Adam and Clare have both the home kit and the away kit.
Clare and Evan have team boots too!
Who has the most items of kit? _____

/1

60. Louise's house is due north of the cafe and north-east of the pier.
The funfair is due west of Louise's house and due north of the pier.
These four places form the points of a square.
Where is the cafe in relation to the funfair? _____

/1

/60

PAPER 2

In the following sentences, a word of **four letters** is hidden across the **end** of one word and the **start** of the next word. Write the hidden word on the line provided. The letter order **cannot** be changed.

Example

The shop was la**st op**en on Tuesday.   *stop*

1. We were effortless winners!   _____

2. You have not asked me to your wedding.   _____

3. I don't like fancy drinks, just plain champagne. _____

4. The sound of that swinging pendulum puts me off. _____

5. What a putrid egg smell!   _____

6. That flower's stamen used to be green.   _____

/6

These **four** words have been written as **number codes**, but one of the codes is missing. The words and codes are not necessarily in the same order. Write the answers to the questions on the lines provided.

RATE   RENT   TEST   MINT
4625   3925   4856

7. Pick out the code for RENT.   _____

8. Pick out the word with the number code 4856.   _____

9. Pick out the code for MINT.   _____

10. What is the code for MARE?   _____

/4

Move **one** letter from the first word and add it to the second word to make two new words. Do **not** arrange any other letters. Write **both** new words, which **must make sense**, on the lines provided.

Example

table   reed   →   _tale_   _breed_

11. coot men   →   _____   _____

12. trust pun   →   _____   _____

13. head slim   →   _____   _____

14. chats ache   →   _____   _____

15. slows side   →   _____   _____

/5

The pairs of words below are linked in some way. Write, on the answer line provided, the word that completes the second pair, following the same pattern as the first.

Example

GOOSE is to GOOD as MOOSE is to _MOOD_

16. COIN is to LOIN as CAKE is to _____

17. FLAVOUR is to FAVOUR as CLOVER is to _____

18. YARD is to DRAY as LIVED is to _____

19. EARTH is to THE as TARTAN is to _____

/4

Rearrange **all** the capital letters to form a correctly spelt word that will complete these sentences sensibly. Write the word on the answer line.

Example

His pet rabbit was hungry so he fed him a juicy TOCARR.   _CARROT_

20. My uncle drives a farm ROTTARC.   _____

21. That one's out of stock; how about an EVTALENRAIT?   _____

22. He was facing CLAIFINNA ruin.   _____

23. What a REPSOURTEPOS idea!   _____

/4

Underline the **two** words, **one** from each set, that are **opposite in meaning.**

Example

(talk run <u>whisper</u>)   (sprint <u>shout</u> speak)

24. (tall, broad, few)   (over, short, wide)

25. (smiling, thoughtful, aloof)   (concerned, friendly, afraid)

26. (substantial, proud, grateful)   (modest, immense, reserved)

/3

Underline the **two** words, **one** from each set, that will complete each sentence in the most sensible way.

Example

Head is to (face, arm, <u>neck</u>) as foot is to (<u>leg</u>, knee, thigh).

27. Kitchen is to (painting, cooking, cleaning) as bathroom is to (washing, mopping, dancing).

28. Word is to (sentence, letter, newspaper) as page is to (write, poem, book).

29. Station is to (wait, petrol, train) as rank is to (place, taxi, first).

30. Pig is to (excess, wings, pork) as cow is to (nasty, beef, patches).

31. Sire is to (squire, father, teacher) as dam is to (bank, lady, mother).

32. Chapter is to (book, writer, author) as district is to (road, county, street).

/6

The word in capitals has had a group of three letters taken out. These **three** letters spell another word, without rearranging the order. Write the **three-letter** word on the line provided. The sentence needs to make sense.

Example

I like my bacon cooked very CRI   <u>SPY</u>

33. His eyes were full of RS from crying.   _____

34. She was HEANT due to uncertainty.   _____

35. We sometimes have SMS in the summer.   _____

36. I'd love to visit another PLA.   _____

37. I doubt he'll ever reign as G.   _____

/5

Underline the **two** words in each group that are **different** from the others.

Example

<u>potato</u>   lemon   banana   <u>cabbage</u>   strawberry

38. train   rocket   coach   plane   bus

39. van   bus   ferry   train   bicycle

40. chair   shelf   window   carpet   picture

41. coffin   dead   dormant   still   death

42. step   sister   foster   daughter   mother

/5

Find **one** letter that will complete **both** pairs of words, finishing the first word and beginning the second word in each pair. The **same** letter must be used for both pairs of words. Write the letter on the line provided.

Example

pa (<u>t</u>) ap   hi (<u>t</u>) ime

43. ru _____ ow   ta _____ ew

44. les _____ tar   pot _____ tep

45. dea _____ eep   sen _____ rop

46. mach _____ gle   radi _____ mens

/4

In the first set of three words, the middle word has been made from letters in the other two words. Complete the second set of words in the **same** way, to make the missing word, **which must make sense**. Write your answers on the lines provided.

Example

fast (tea) real   leaf (<u>fir</u>) hire

47. role (led) said   near (_____) look

48. rain (yarn) clay   roof (_____) thus

49. crop (crib) bite   fail (_____) edit

50. pool (loup) pout   reef (_____) seep

51. lust (rust) turn   fear (_____) east

/5

Write the number that continues each sequence in the most sensible way.

Example

3   6   12   21   33   *48*

52. 9   10   12   15   19   _____

53. 15   16   18   21   25   _____

54. 3   6   12   24   _____

55. 2   5   11   23   _____

56. 7   10   _____   16   19

/5

Write the words into the grid so they can be read across or down.

Example

YET   EYE   WET   MEW   AYE   MAY

M	A	Y
E	Y	E
W	E	T

57. AYE   EYE   TEG   NAB   NET   BEG

58. OWL   DOE   ADO   APE   POW   EEL

/2

59. Five children, Roger, Lucy, Karl, Meehna and Iris all tried some fruit smoothies at the weekend.

Everyone except Iris tried pineapple.

Four children tried strawberry.

Only Lucy, Karl and Meehna tried banana.

Roger didn't try strawberry.

Iris and Karl were the only children who tried blueberry.

Who tried the fewest smoothies? _____ /1

60. Colin's shop is due west of the Post Office.

The Town Hall is due south of the Post Office.

The library is south-west of the Post Office.

These four places form the points of a square.

Where is Colin's shop in relation to the Town Hall? _____ /1

/60

PAPER 3

In the following sentences, a word of **four letters** is hidden across the **end** of one word and the **start** of the next word. Write the hidden word on the line provided. The letter order **cannot** be changed.

Example

The shop was la**st op**en on Tuesday.   _stop_

1. My lovely cacti mean a lot to me.   _____

2. It was a bizarre addition to the collection.   _____

3. At last, I can bathe now!   _____

4. Being in limbo attracted a lot of attention.   _____

5. The farmer selected a very brisk ewe.   _____

6. Yesterday I bumped into my last husband. _____

7. The dog had a crooked right hind leg. _____

Find the pair of letters that completes the sentence in the most sensible way. The alphabet has been printed below to help you.

A B C D E F G H I J K L M N O P Q R S T U V W X Y Z

Example

BY is to EV as HS is to KP

8. BE is to EH as MP is to (_____)

9. ML is to NO as KJ is to (_____)

10. GE is to HF as IG is to (_____)

Underline the **two** words, **one** from each set, that have a **similar meaning**.

Example

(car, take, jump)   (chair, leap, drive)

11. (waste, place, bin)   (discard, stuff, station)

12. (score, correct, exam)   (answer, test, paper)

13. (faint, drop, collapse)   (doctor, pale, clear)

14. (work, hire, ladder)   (rent, reach, taller)

15. (bird, dive, duck)   (swim, feather, crouch)

Underline the **two** words, **one** from each set, that will complete each sentence in the most sensible way.

Example

Head is to (face, arm, <u>neck</u>) as foot is to (<u>leg</u>, knee, thigh).

16. Fish is to (fins, eyes, scales) as bird is to (ears, claws, wings).

17. Blank is to (barren, ignore, empty) as greet is to (acknowledge, agree, sleep).

18. Team is to (swarm, gather, player) as crowd is to (fan, push, crush).

19. Hesitant is to (sure, confident, uncertain) as spin is to (twirl, positive, dance).

20. Nocturnal is to (day, dog, bat) as diurnal is to (pigeon, afternoon, badger).

/5

The word in capitals has had a group of three letters taken out. These **three** letters spell another word, without rearranging the order. Write the **three-letter** word on the line provided. The sentence needs to make sense.

Example

I like my bacon cooked very CRI   <u>SPY</u>

21. What a noisy GLE of geese!   _____

22. Help yourself to a cold DR.   _____

23. The room was painted too OGE for her taste!   _____

24. BEE of falling rocks!   _____

25. The low flying dove skimmed the church SPLE. _____

/5

Underline the **two** words in each group that are **different** from the others.

Example

<u>potato</u>   lemon   banana   <u>cabbage</u>   strawberry

26. rose   tomato   carrot   daffodil   turnip

27. wren   kestrel   chaffinch   sparrowhawk   starling

28. loudly   dream   sleep   quietly   snore

29. grass   carpet   ceiling   floor   roof

30. sheep   mutton   pig   beef   cow

/5

Underline the **two** words, **one** from each set, that when put together, make one new, correctly spelt word. The order of the letters does not change. **The word from the group on the left always comes first.**

Example

(run, <u>use</u>, give)   (take, <u>less</u>, red)

31. (bee, be, in)   (good, mean, hind)

32. (red, black, chimney)   (bored, board, soot)

33. (clever, head, cap)   (size, wise, us)

34. (mate, neck, pal)   (ace, less, ping)

35. (poker, man, smoker)   (men, able, age)

36. (clap, run, quick)   (like, less, ping)

/6

Find **one** letter that will complete **both** pairs of words, finishing the first word and beginning the second word in each pair. The **same** letter must be used for both pairs of words. Write the letter on the line provided.

Example

pa (<u>t</u>) ap   hi (<u>t</u>) ime

37. hi _____ ie   ha _____ ap

38. dia _____ awn   vei _____ oan

39. sur _____ jord   decaf _____ lute

40. tax _____ ris   khak _____ cily

/4

Underline **one** word from the list in brackets that goes equally well with both pairs of words outside the brackets.

Example

(ribbon, <u>present</u>, play, theatre, party)

gift, token   show, demonstrate

41. (brow, pupil, cake, tear, water)

   eye, droplet   rip, slice

42. (shut, own, offer, near, intimate)

   close, personal   hint, suggest

43. (drawing, pre-empt, design, build, unique)

   pattern, plan   invent, create

44. (food, produce, fruit, gift, show)

   apple, pears   present, appear

/4

Letters stand for numbers. Work out the answer to each sum. Write your answer as a **letter** on the line provided.

Example

If $A = 2, B = 3, C = 4, D = 5, E = 6, F = 8$

what is the answer to this sum written as a letter: $D + B = $ <u>F</u>

If $A = 3, B = 5, C = 6, D = 8, E = 10$, what is:

45. $E + A - B = $ _____

46. $D + A - C = $ _____

47. $E - B + A = $ _____

48. $D - C + A = $ _____

49. $C + B - A = $ _____

/5

Find the missing **pair of letters** in the series.
The alphabet is provided to help you.

A B C D E F G H I J K L M N O P Q R S T U V W X Y Z

Example

MO   MK   OQ   KI   _QS_

50. YZ   BA   WX   DC   UV   FE   _____

51. CA   DB   EC   FD   GE   HF   _____

52. ZX   YW   XV   WU   VT   US   _____

53. NA   OC   PE   QG   RI   SK   _____

54. MZ   LX   KV   JT   IR   HP   _____

/5

Write the number that continues each sequence in the most sensible way.

Example

3   6   12   21   33   _48_

55. 4   7   13   22   34   _____

56. 5   9   17   33   _____

57. 9   18   36   72   _____

/3

Write the words into the grid so they can be read across or down.

Example

YET   EYE   WET   MEW   AYE   MAY

M	A	Y
E	Y	E
W	E	T

58. YET   NET   AYE   FAY   EYE   FEN

/1

59. During Summer Camp, five children, Paul, Simon, Linda, Dan and Ursula all tried a variety of activities.

Paul, Simon and Dan did some painting.

Three children did archery.

Dan and Paul didn't bother with archery.

Who did the most activities? _____

/1

60. The park is south-west of the cafe and due south of Pam's shop.

The museum is due south of the cafe.

Pam's shop is due west of the cafe.

These four places form the points of a square.

Where is Pam's shop in relation to the museum? _____

/1

/60

PAPER 4

In the following sentences, a word of **four letters** is hidden across the **end** of one word and the **start** of the next word. Write the hidden word on the line provided. The letter order **cannot** be changed.

Example

The shop was la**st op**en on Tuesday.   *stop*

1. I sweep airport floors for a living.   _____

2. Can a baron certify my status?   _____

3. I could also leap up high.   _____

4. What great heydays we all had! _____

5. I never understood her past hatred of me. _____

6. I love our great history! _____

/6

Move **one** letter from the first word and add it to the second word to make two new words. Do **not** rearrange any other letters. Write **both** new words, which **must make sense**, on the lines provided.

Example

ta**b**le   reed   →   _tale_   _**b**reed_

7. bound for   →   _____   _____

8. brand cab   →   _____   _____

9. cache all   →   _____   _____

10. cadge bar   →   _____   _____

11. calms one   →   _____   _____

/5

Change the first word of the third pair in the same way as the other pairs to give a new word. Write the answer on the line provided.

Example

tray, dray   tram, dram   trip, _drip_

12. bard, drab   devil, lived   sleep, _____

13. find, fund   pint, punt   silk, _____

14. rate, rat   mate, mat   hate, _____

15. noter, toner   ropes, pores   risen, _____

16. tab, bat   gel, leg   are, _____

/5

21

Underline the words that are made from the same letters.

Example

NAN   NAP   <u>WON</u>   WOW   <u>NOW</u>

17. PIT   POT   HIP   TIP   HOP   PUT

18. ARISE   SIREN   STAIR   AREAS   RAISE   RISEN

19. PESTS   STEEP   STEPS   SEEPS   PEEPS   SEATS

/3

Underline the **two** words, **one** from each set, that have a **similar meaning**.

Example

(car, take, <u>jump</u>)   (chair, <u>leap</u>, drive)

20. (wolf, howl, moon)   (paw, round, devour)

21. (mourn, grass, late)   (dawn, early, grieve)

22. (screw, sink, adapt)   (alter, plumb, altar)

23. (drum, banjo, music)   (strings, piano, guitar)

24. (bendy, measure, break)   (flexible, snapped, ruler)

/5

The word in capitals has had a group of three letters taken out. These
three letters spell another word, without rearranging the order. Write the
three-letter word on the line provided. The sentence needs to make sense.

Example

I like my bacon cooked very CRI   <u>SPY</u>

25. You need a pencil and some PR to draw.   _____

26. Can I take a SER as I'm all sweaty?   _____

27. They really hoped the GAE could fix it!   _____

28. I don't like the way he WED at me!   _____

29. My old flat used to have a MO.   _____

/5

Underline the **two** words in each group that are **different** from the others.

Example

<u>potato</u>   lemon   banana   <u>cabbage</u>   strawberry

30. remarkable   ordinary   outstanding   magnificent   average

31. scorpion   gnat   beetle   spider   ant

32. whistle   lips   teeth   smile   tongue

33. toe   arm   knuckle   finger   elbow

34. kettle   snare   bass   saucepan   dish

/5

Underline the **two** words, **one** from each set, that when put together, make one new correctly spelt word. The order of the letters does not change. **The word from the group on the left always comes first.**

Example

(run, <u>use</u>, give)   (take, <u>less</u>, red)

35. (air, train, plane)   (sky, spray, port)

36. (never, over, hang)   (ore, or, awe)

37. (suit, quick, thought)   (more, able, wise)

38. (large, over, under)   (toe, feet, tow)

39. (queen, silver, royal)   (jubilee, ware, where)

/5

In the first set of three words, the middle word has been made from letters in the other two words. Complete the second set of words in the **same** way, to make the missing word, **which must make sense**. Write your answers on the lines provided.

Example

fast (tea) real   leaf (<u>fir</u>) hire

40. prod (ore) rise   node (_____) cite

41. auto (undo) done   evil (_____) ices

42. done (dead) hard   lake (_____) seek

23

43. gene (rage) near   flee (_____) teas

44. neon (none) noon   oral (_____) pool

/5

> Letters stand for numbers. Work out the answer to each sum. Write your answer as a **letter** on the line provided.

Example

If A = 2, B = 3, C = 4, D = 5, E = 6, F = 8

what is the answer to this sum written as a letter: D + B = F

If A = 2, B = 5, C = 8, D = 10, E = 16, what is:

45. D + C – A = _____

46. B + C + B – A = _____

47. (A × C) – C = _____

/4

48. E – D + A = _____

> Find the missing **pairs of letters** in the series. The alphabet is provided to help you.

A B C D E F G H I J K L M N O P Q R S T U V W X Y Z

Example

AD   CF   EH   GJ   IL   KN

49. _____   ML   KJ   IH   GF   _____

50. _____   DE   GH   JK   MN   _____

51. _____   ON   LK   IH   FE   _____

52. _____   NO   KJ   PQ   IH   _____

53. _____   BY   CX   DW   EV   _____

/5

> Write the numbers that continue each sequence in the most sensible way.

Example

12   14   16   18   20   22

54. 3   8   _____   18   _____

55. 11   22   _____   _____   176   352

56. 8   _____   32   64   _____   256

57. 61   15   63   13   _____   _____

/4

> Write the words into the grid so they can be read across or down.

Example

YET   EYE   WET   MEW   AYE   MAY

M	A	Y
E	Y	E
W	E	T

58. EYE   YEN   LAY   TEN   LET   AYE

/1

59. Julie, Rupinder, David, Jane and Sangeet all keep pets.

Julie, Rupinder and David all have a dog.

Two children have a goldfish.

Rupinder and David have a cat.

Jane, Julie and Sangeet all own a hamster whilst Rupinder and David each have a parrot.

Julie, David and Sangeet do not have a goldfish.

Who has the most pets? _____

/1

60. Graham's garage is due east of the bridge and due north of the office block.

The bridge is north-west of the office block.

The flyover is due south of the bridge.

Where is Graham's garage in relation to the flyover?

Write your answer on the line provided. _____

/1

/60

PAPER 5

Move **one** letter from the first word and add it to the second word to make two new words. Do **not** rearrange any other letters. Write **both** new words, which **must make sense**, on the lines provided.

Example

table   reed   →   _tale_   _breed_

1. tired use   →   _____   _____

2. hear wet   →   _____   _____

3. kill sin   →   _____   _____

4. boast rat   →   _____   _____

5. borne ego   →   _____   _____

6. towed here   →   _____   _____

/6

Work out the code for each question. The alphabet is here to help you.

A B C D E F G H I J K L M N O P Q R S T U V W X Y Z

Example

If the code for DUCK is EVDL, what is the code for SWAN?   _TXBO_

7. If the code for BLUE is YIRB, what is the code for GREEN?   _____

8. If the code for CLAY is YHWU, what is the code for SAND?   _____

9. If the code for LIGHT is HECDP, what is the code for DARK?   _____

10. If the code for BLACK is EODFN, what does ZKLWH mean?   _____

/4

Find the pair of letters that completes the sentence in the most sensible way. The alphabet has been printed below to help you.

> A B C D E F G H I J K L M N O P Q R S T U V W X Y Z

Example

BY is to EV as HS is to <u>KP</u>

11. AC is to BD as IK is to _____

12. DW is to FU as HS is to _____

13. WV is to UX as ML is to _____

14. HZ is to YG as FX is to _____

/4

Underline the **two** words, **one** from each set, that have a **similar meaning**.

Example

(car, take, <u>jump</u>)   (chair, <u>leap</u>, drive)

15. (committed, shout, swear)   (promise, rude, profane)

16. (slow, brief, shorts)   (pants, short, wear)

17. (chair, kitchen, counter)   (sit, table, seat)

18. (shiny, clamp, car)   (grip, fine, parking)

19. (drug, anxious, crave)   (need, despair, desperate)

/5

Underline the **two** words, **one** from each set, that are **opposite in meaning**.

Example

(talk, run, <u>whisper)</u>   (sprint, <u>shout,</u> speak)

20. (eager, school, hospital)   (pupil, willing, patient)

21. (engage, exhale, vacant)   (marry, occupied, insert)

22. (pulsing, perpetual, survival)   (finite, alive, diminishing)

/3

Underline the **two** words, **one** from each set, that will complete each sentence in the most sensible way.

Example

Head is to (face, arm, <u>neck</u>) as foot is to (<u>leg</u>, knee, thigh).

23. Television is to (enjoy, family, watch) as radio is to (listen, friends, fun).

24. Beetle is to (insect, wings, six) as spider is to (fly, eight, wings).

25. Snake is to (slither, scales, reptile) as mouse is to (rat, eyes, mammal).

26. Bear is to (burden, furry, naked) as snake is to (twist, slither, scaly).

27. Duvet is to (bed, quilt, sheet) as speedy is to (sloth, fast, tortoise).

28. Gregarious is to (awake, lively, generous) as introverted is to (shy, noisy, receptive).

/6

Underline the **two** words in each group that are **different** from the others.

Example

<u>potato</u>   lemon   banana   <u>cabbage</u>   strawberry

29. speak   shout   show   say   mime

30. wheat   tractor   oats   barley   horse

31. milk   cheese   bread   butter   toast

32. hamster   mouse   wheel   keyboard   screen

33. fly   float   swim   walk   dive

/5

Underline the **two** words, **one** from each set, that when put together, make one new correctly spelt word. The order of the letters does not change. **The word from the group on the left always comes first.**

Example

(run, <u>use</u>, give)   (take, <u>less</u>, red)

34. (you, jig, we)   (saw, sore, dance)

35. (bee, wasp, sure)   (line, hind, side)

36. (not, sea, hand)   (shore, sand, sure)

37. (man, deaf, cad)   (die, less, lass)

38. (bat, bet, but)   (tan, ten, tonne)

Find **one** letter that will complete **both** pairs of words, finishing the first word and beginning the second word in each pair. The **same** letter must be used for both pairs of words. Write the letter on the line provided.

Example

pa (t) ap   hi (t) ime

39. to (_____) it   ra (_____) aw

40. ruf (_____) ear   tur (_____) arm

41. lass (_____) ust   curi (_____) boe

42. lyri (_____) rude   atti (_____) hurl

In the first set of three words, the middle word has been made from letters in the other two words. Complete the second set of words in the **same** way, to make the missing word, **which must make sense**. Write your answers on the lines provided.

Example

fast (tea) real   leaf (fir) hire

43. stud (let) lime   slow (_____) plea

44. rota (late) seal   logo (_____) malt

45. owls (lots) mist   acne (_____) step

46. nine (earn) dear   seek (_____) slap

47. nine (dine) ride   rain (_____) peer

Letters stand for numbers. Work out the answer to each sum. Write your answer as a **letter** on the line provided.

Example

If A = 2, B = 3, C = 4, D = 5, E = 6, F = 8

what is the answer to this sum written as a letter: D + B = <u>F</u>

If A = 2, B = 3, C = 4, D = 9, E = 12, what is:

48. (B × C) – B = _____

49. (D ÷ B) × C = _____

50. (B × E) ÷ D = _____

/4

51. (C × D) ÷ E = _____

Write the number that continues each sequence in the most sensible way.

Example

| 6 | 12 | 21 | 33 | <u>48</u> |

52. 1   8   22   50   _____

53. 1   5   13   29   _____

54. 3   8   18   38   _____

55. 7   12   22   42   _____

/5

56. 3   5   9   15   23   _____

Write the words into the grid so they can be read across or down.

Example

YET   EYE   WET   MEW   AYE   MAY

M	A	Y
E	Y	E
W	E	T

57. EMU   PEA   PUT   PIP   IMP   APT

58. GNU   EON   EGG   NUT   ONE   GET

/2

59. Sara, Jon, Dimitri, Aaron and Evie all love to listen to music!

Jon, Dimitri and Evie are fans of rock, whilst Sara and Dimitri both like hip-hop.

Aaron, Sara and Jon like pop, and Evie and Sara like classical.

Who only likes pop? _____

/1

60. Julie's bookshop is due south of the Health Centre.

The Health Centre is north-west of the vet and due north of Julie's bookshop.

The school is due east of the Health Centre.

These four places form the points of a square.

Where is Julie's bookshop in relation to the school? _____

/1

/60

PAPER 6

In the following sentences, a word of **four letters** is hidden across the **end** of one word and the **start** of the next word. Write the hidden word on the line provided. The letter order **cannot** be changed.

Example:

The shop was la**st op**en on Tuesday.   _stop_

1. We shop every day!   _____

2. In Maths, we'll study volume after we've done area.   _____

3. I like to count my cotton every morning!   _____

4. He gave his mother a Christmas kiss!   _____

5. We all have a right to public education.   _____

6. I keep thinking I've seen that man everywhere!   _____

/6

Move **one** letter from the first word and add it to the second word to make two new words. Do **not** rearrange any other letters. Write **both** new words, which **must make sense**, on the lines provided.

Example

table   reed   →   _tale_   _breed_

7. aunty our   →   _____   _____

8. spout men   →   _____   _____

9. arena spa   →   _____   _____

10. cello filed   →   _____   _____

11. crock harm   →   _____   _____

12. tasks high   →   _____   _____

/6

Work out the code for each question. The alphabet is here to help you.

A B C D E F G H I J K L M N O P Q R S T U V W X Y Z

Example

If the code for DUCK is EVDL, what is the code for SWAN? <u>TXBO</u>

13. If the code for DRILL is AOFII, what is the code for NAIL? _____

14. If the code for HANDS is EXKAP, what is the code for FEET? _____

15. If the code for CARPET is FDUSHW, what does OLQR mean? _____

16. If the code for DESKS is GHVNV, what does FKDLUV mean? _____

/4

Change the first word of the third pair in the same way as the other pairs to give a new word. Write the answer on the line provided.

Example

tray, dray   tram, dram   trip, <u>drip</u>

17. ride, rid   rode, rod   bide, _____

18. loot, tool   tram, mart   room, _____

19. dare, read   dale, lead   lame, _____

20. cool, look   gran, nark   flaw, _____

/4

Underline the **two** words, **one** from each set, that have a **similar meaning**.

Example

(car, take, <u>jump</u>)   (chair, <u>leap</u>, drive)

21. (pot, grind, salt)   (ice, crush, pepper)

22. (blow, trade, sky)   (business, winds, cloud)

23. (sing, noisy, logo)   (music, sign, song)

24. (mountain, attempted, realised)   (achieved, goal, summit)

25. (brain, nerve, pain)   (brave, courage, vein)

/5

Underline the **two** words, **one** from each set, that are **opposite in meaning.**

Example

(talk, run, <u>whisper)</u>   (sprint, <u>shout,</u> speak)

26. (chance, lucky, surprise)   (unfortunate, knowing, win)

27. (vivacious, night, nostalgic)   (twilight, innocuous, quiet)

28. (damp, freezing, cool)   (light, moist, boiling)

/3

The word in capitals has had a group of three letters taken out. These **three** letters spell another word, without rearranging the order. Write the **three-letter** word on the line provided. The sentence needs to make sense.

Example

I like my bacon cooked very CRI   _SPY_

29. I need more SP to put all my things in!   _____

30. A MER can be a useful tool.   _____

31. Must you DISCAGE me?   _____

32. Another word for peaceful is TQUIL.   _____

33. It's too CEFUL for me!   _____

/5

Underline the **two** words, **one** from each set, that when put together, make one new correctly spelt word. The order of the letters does not change. **The word from the group on the left always comes first.**

Example

(run, <u>use</u>, give)   (take, <u>less</u>, red)

34. (cream, butter, milk)   (jam, flee, fly)

35. (smoke, pan, dust)   (ache, mop, ash)

36. (right, then, hence)   (fore, forth, fourth)

37. (foot, feet, abouts)   (ride, wear, where)

38. (new, day, early)   (morn, born, bourne)

/5

Underline **one** word from the list in brackets that goes equally well with both pairs of words outside the brackets.

Example

(ribbon, present, play, theatre, party)

gift, token   show, demonstrate

39. (soar, transport, van, movement, drive)

    bus, car   swim, fly

40. (correct, brilliant, absolute, church, money)

    right, perfect   alter, change

41. (story, end, deduce, kill, position)

    beginning, middle   conclude, terminate

42. (neuron, space, trouble, bother, matter)

    particle, atom   concern, worry

/4

In the first set of three words, the middle word has been made from letters in the other two words. Complete the second set of words in the **same** way, to make the missing word, **which must make sense**. Write your answers on the lines provided.

Example

fast (tea) real   leaf (fir) hire

43. slid (ale) game   cite (_____) drip

44. lock (crow) grew   harp (_____) door

45. hair (said) dogs   fine (_____) door

46. were (brew) beer   tray (_____) ways

47. saws (pews) seep   sews (_____) rows

/5

Letters stand for numbers. Work out the answer to each sum. Write your answer as a **letter** on the line provided.

Example

If A = 2, B = 3, C = 4, D = 5, E = 6, F = 8

what is the answer to this sum written as a letter: D + B = $\underline{F}$

If A = 2, B = 4, C = 8, D = 10, E = 16, what is:

48. (B × C) ÷ A = _____

49. (D + C − A) ÷ B = _____

50. (A × D) − (C × A) = _____

51. (B × A × B) ÷ E = _____

/4

Write the numbers that continue each sequence in the most sensible way.

Example

12	14	16	18	20	22

52. 9 _____ 17 _____ 25

53. _____ 18 36 _____ 144 288

54. 5 _____ 45 135 _____ 1215

55. 448 3 112 2 _____ _____ 7

/5

56. 7 308 14 154 _____ _____ 56

Write the words into the grid so they can be read across or down.

Example

YET   EYE   WET   MEW   AYE   MAY

M	A	Y
E	Y	E
W	E	T

57. ERA   MET   ORE   GOB   GEM   BAT

58. OAR   OWL   WRY   LEE   RYE   ARE

/2

59. Charlie, Sasha, Deepa, Liam and Sophie all bring packed lunches to school.

Four of the five children have sandwiches.

Sasha and Liam have a chocolate biscuit.

Sophie and Charlie have a pasta salad.

Deepa and Liam have a packet of crisps each.

Sophie did not have any sandwiches.

Only Charlie did not have a piece of fruit.

Who had the most things for lunch? _____

/1

60. The stables are due east of the puppet theatre.

The puppet theatre is north-west of the playground.

The playground is due south of the stables and due east of Olivia's toyshop.

These four places form the points of a square.

Where is Olivia's toyshop in relation to the stables? _____

/1

/60

PAPER 7

These **four** words have been written as **number codes**, but one of the codes is missing. The words and codes are not necessarily in the same order. Write the answers to the questions on the lines provided.

BLUNT   BLUSH   BLITZ   BLINK

45362   45987   45906

1. Pick out the code for BLUSH.   _____

2. Pick out the word with the number code 45362.   _____

3. Pick out the code for BLUNT.   _____

4. What is the code for SUITS?   _____

/4

Move **one** letter from the first word and add it to the second word to make two new words. Do **not** rearrange any other letters. Write **both** new words, which **must make sense**, on the lines provided.

Example

table   reed   →   _ta<u>le</u>_   _<u>b</u>reed_

5. off ire   →   _____   _____

6. pan lea   →   _____   _____

7. batch hat   →   _____   _____

8. began low   →   _____   _____

9. bale all   →   _____   _____

10. bilge ore   →   _____   _____

/6

Answer booklet: More Verbal Reasoning age 10–11

Paper 1
1. thus
2. best
3. nest
4. rage
5. hiss
6. grin
7. **e** trip, hate/heat *or* **t** ripe, that
8. **g** ear, king
9. **n** blow, none
10. **b** less, vibe
11. **d** cane, dream
12. CAKE
13. SHOCK
14. HANGER
15. PLAIN
16. stony
17. splits
18. cyclone
19. enemy
20. talk, chat
21. bawl, cry *or* bowl, throw
22. lone, solo
23. cement, glue
24. foam, froth
25. BAT bathroom
26. RUB scrubbed
27. CAR carpet
28. PAT pattern
29. NIT ignite
30. grumpy, sad
31. blaring, rowdy
32. soft, crunchy
33. greens, spinach
34. brake, came
35. capable
36. manage
37. damping *or* clamping
38. haulage
39. damage
40. needle
41. leaves
42. object
43. trade
44. cat
45. nail
46. star
47. tied
48. deck
49. C
50. C
51. B
52. C
53. D
54. 1, 4
55. 8, 17
56. 32, 45
57. 29, 92
58. 11, 23
59. Clare
60. south-east

Paper 2
1. reef *or* ewer
2. task
3. inch
4. lump *or* hats
5. ride *or* eggs
6. menu
7. 4625
8. RATE
9. 3925
10. 3846
11. **o** cot, omen
12. **t** rust, punt
13. **e** had, slime
14. **c** hats, cache *or* **s** chat, aches
15. **l** sows, sidle/slide *or* **s** lows/slow, sides
16. LAKE
17. COVER
18. DEVIL
19. ANT
20. TRACTOR
21. ALTERNATIVE
22. FINANCIAL
23. PREPOSTEROUS
24. tall, short
25. aloof, friendly
26. substantial, modest
27. cooking, washing
28. sentence, book
29. train, taxi
30. pork, beef
31. sire, dam
32. book, county
33. TEA tears
34. SIT hesitant
35. TOR storms
36. NET planet
37. KIN king
38. rocket, plane
39. van, bicycle
40. chair, carpet
41. coffin, death
42. step, foster
43. ru<u>n</u> <u>n</u>ow, ta<u>n</u> <u>n</u>ew
44. les<u>s</u> <u>s</u>tar, pot<u>s</u> <u>s</u>tep
45. dea<u>d</u> <u>d</u>eep, sen<u>d</u> <u>d</u>rop
46. mach<u>o</u> <u>o</u>gle, radi<u>o</u> <u>o</u>mens
47. ark
48. surf
49. fade
50. fees
51. sear
52. 24
53. 30
54. 48
55. 47
56. 13

57.

N	E	T
A	Y	E
B	E	G

(answers may vary as the positioning of the grid can change)

58.

A	D	O
P	O	W
E	E	L

(answers may vary as the positioning of the grid can change)

59. Roger
60. north-west

Paper 3
1. time *or* tome
2. read *or* onto
3. then
4. boat
5. skew
6. thus *or* dint
7. thin
8. PS
9. PQ *or* LM
10. JH
11. bin, discard
12. exam, test
13. faint, pale
14. hire, rent
15. duck, crouch
16. fins, wings
17. ignore, acknowledge
18. player, fan
19. uncertain, twirl
20. bat, pigeon
21. GAG gaggle
22. INK drink
23. RAN orange
24. WAR beware
25. TEE steeple
26. rose, daffodil
27. kestrel, sparrowhawk
28. loudly, quietly
29. ceiling, roof
30. mutton, beef
31. behind
32. blackboard
33. capsize
34. palace
35. manage
36. clapping
37. hi<u>t</u> <u>t</u>ie, ha<u>t</u> <u>t</u>ap
38. dia<u>l</u> <u>l</u>awn, vei<u>l</u> <u>l</u>oan
39. sur<u>f</u> <u>f</u>jord, decaf<u>f</u> <u>f</u>lute
40. tax<u>i</u> <u>i</u>ris, khak<u>i</u> <u>i</u>cily
41. tear
42. intimate
43. design
44. produce
45. D
46. B
47. D

48. B
49. D
50. ST
51. IG
52. TR
53. TM
54. GN
55. 49
56. 65
57. 144
58.

F	E	N
A	Y	E
Y	E	T

(answers may vary as the positioning of the grid can change)

59. Simon
60. north-west

Paper 4

1. pair
2. once
3. sole
4. they
5. that
6. this
7. **u** bond, four
8. **r** band, crab
9. **c** ache, call
10. **d** cage, bard
11. **c** alms, cone/once *or* **s** calm, ones
12. peels
13. sulk
14. hat
15. siren
16. era
17. TIP
18. RAISE
19. STEPS
20. wolf, devour
21. mourn, grieve
22. adapt, alter
23. banjo, guitar
24. bendy, flexible
25. APE paper
26. HOW shower
27. RAG garage
28. INK winked
29. USE mouse
30. ordinary, average
31. scorpion, spider
32. whistle, smile
33. knuckle, elbow
34. saucepan, dish
35. airport
36. overawe
37. suitable
38. undertow
39. silverware
40. doe
41. veil
42. leek *or* keel
43. safe
44. poor
45. E
46. E
47. C
48. C
49. ON, ED
50. AB, PQ
51. RQ, CB
52. ML, RS
53. AZ, FU
54. 13, 23
55. 44, 88
56. 16, 128
57. 65, 11
58.

L	A	Y
E	Y	E
T	E	N

(answers may vary as the positioning of the grid can change)

59. Rupinder
60. north-east

Paper 5

1. **d** tire, used *or* **r** tied, user/ruse
2. **h** ear, whet
3. **k** ill, sink/skin
4. **s** boat, rats *or* **b** oast, brat
5. **r** bone, ergo
6. **t** owed, there *or* **w** toed, where
7. DOBBK
8. OWJZ
9. ZWNG
10. WHITE
11. JL
12. JQ
13. KN
14. WE
15. swear, promise
16. brief, short
17. chair, seat
18. clamp, grip
19. crave, need
20. eager, patient
21. vacant, occupied
22. perpetual, finite
23. watch, listen
24. six, eight
25. reptile, mammal
26. furry, scaly
27. quilt, fast
28. lively, shy
29. show, mime
30. tractor, horse
31. bread, toast
32. hamster, wheel
33. fly, walk
34. jigsaw
35. beeline
36. seashore
37. caddie
38. batten
39. top pit, rap paw
40. ruff fear, turf farm
41. lasso oust, curio, oboe
42. lyric crude, attic churl
43. pal
44. toga
45. nape
46. laps
47. earn
48. D
49. E
50. C
51. B
52. 106
53. 61
54. 78
55. 82
56. 33
57.

P	I	P
E	M	U
A	P	T

(answers may vary as the positioning of the grid can change)

58.

E	G	G
O	N	E
N	U	T

(answers may vary as the positioning of the grid can change)

59. Aaron
60. south-west

Paper 6

1. hope
2. near
3. tone
4. mask
5. lice *or* iced
6. mane
7. **y** aunt, your
8. **u** spot, menu or **s** pout, mens
9. **n** area, span
10. **o** cell, foiled
11. **c** rock, charm
12. **t** asks, thigh or **s** task, highs
13. KXFI
14. CBBQ
15. LINO
16. CHAIRS
17. bid
18. moor
19. meal
20. walk
21. grind, crush
22. trade, business
23. logo, sign
24. realised, achieved
25. nerve, courage
26. lucky, unfortunate
27. vivacious, quiet
28. freezing, boiling
29. ACE space
30. HAM hammer
31. OUR discourage
32. RAN tranquil
33. PEA peaceful
34. butterfly
35. panache
36. henceforth
37. footwear
38. newborn
39. movement
40. correct
41. end
42. matter
43. rip
44. roar
45. rind
46. wart
47. sows
48. E
49. B
50. B
51. A
52. 13, 21
53. 9, 72

54. 15, 405
55. 28, 1
56. 28, 77

57.
G	O	B
E	R	A
M	E	T

(answers may vary as the positioning of the grid can change)

58.
O	W	L
A	R	E
R	Y	E

(answers may vary as the positioning of the grid can change)

59. Liam
60. south-west

Paper 7
1. 45987
2. BLITZ
3. 45906
4. 89368
5. **f** of, fire
6. **p** an, plea/leap
7. **c** bath, chat
8. **g** bean, glow
9. **b** ale, ball
10. **g** bile, gore/ogre
11. VFDUI
12. SGIER
13. KMJX
14. BEAST
15. SNUFF
16. STAR
17. GRUDGE
18. LANE
19. SHADE
20. TWITS
21. METRE
22. dinky, cute
23. exit, leave
24. coach, trainer
25. trade, exchange
26. vain, conceited
27. FOR forest
28. URN turns
29. WIN winter
30. THE their
31. IRE fire
32. primrose
33. becalm
34. behalf
35. robbed *or* drinker
36. bather
37. coo<u>t</u> <u>t</u>ube, wil<u>t</u> <u>t</u>our
38. wor<u>k</u> <u>k</u>ing, lic<u>k</u> <u>k</u>een
39. yet<u>i</u> <u>i</u>odine, corg<u>i</u> <u>i</u>ota
40. lie<u>u</u> <u>u</u>ltra, bayo<u>u</u> <u>u</u>sher
41. dab
42. dodo
43. tars
44. earn
45. rage
46. B
47. D
48. A
49. D
50. A
51. 35
52. 61

---

53. 14
54. 21
55. 3
56. 15
57. 25

58.
P	A	D
E	R	E
N	E	W

(answers may vary as the positioning of the grid can change)

59. Paige
60. north-east

Paper 8
1. sink
2. seat
3. fall *or* sand
4. form
5. vent
6. tire
7. rose
8. deer
9. lair
10. teased
11. cherub
12. octanes
13. boy, man
14. spots, stripes
15. intelligent, sneaky
16. grams, metres
17. harsh, participant
18. LAY delayed
19. EAT heather
20. USE trousers
21. RAN grand
22. HER leather
23. cotton, wool
24. oboe, drum
25. danger, concern
26. raspberry, strawberry
27. scales, bath
28. farmyard
29. insect
30. bathe
31. beached
32. antics
33. group
34. book
35. reflect
36. page
37. new
38. rear *or* rake
39. dine
40. earn
41. rare
42. C
43. E
44. B
45. D
46. F
47. A
48. EL
49. VS
50. QR
51. GT
52. AA
53. 29
54. 90
55. 26
56. 13

---

57. 7
58. 13
59. C
60. south-west

Paper 9
1. 72545
2. GIRLS
3. 72348
4. 58234
5. **s** play, send/ends *or* **l** pays, lend
6. **s** kid, sees *or* **d** ski, seed
7. **s** pike, pins/spin
8. **e** breath, tube
9. **i** defy, waive
10. **l** axe, clamp
11. UNKEG
12. QEGCP
13. LAKE
14. TAIL
15. VY
16. KQ
17. HL *or* TX
18. PR
19. quit, leave
20. winch, lift
21. way, direction
22. paste, stick
23. prime, main
24. foot, hand
25. human, cat
26. accept, impress
27. habitat, puzzle
28. bees, cattle
29. MET comet
30. EAR early
31. EAT sweaty
32. OLD gold
33. ATE state
34. bre<u>d</u> <u>d</u>am, bar<u>d</u> <u>d</u>uos
35. dea<u>f</u> <u>f</u>uel, clif<u>f</u> <u>f</u>ool
36. tho<u>u</u> <u>u</u>rban, burea<u>u</u> <u>u</u>surp
37. catc<u>h</u> <u>h</u>url, tras<u>h</u> <u>h</u>airy
38. sad
39. teen
40. avid
41. lint
42. pair
43. ZA, UF
44. AW, FC
45. ZD, UX
46. AD, IL
47. ZW, XU
48. 19
49. 54
50. 8
51. 3
52. -16
53. deer
54. diving
55. ghoul
56. mule
57. atom

58.
T	O	D
A	N	Y
P	E	E

(answers may vary as the positioning of the grid can change)

59. Carl
60. south-west

Paper 10
1. tall *or* nowt
2. find
3. hear
4. turn
5. when
6. then
7. AYR
8. HMFSHJ
9. KTTI
10. EARTH
11. FAKE
12. SWIMMING
13. BETS
14. HEARD
15. direct
16. eclair
17. smell, odour
18. sick, ill
19. wind, twist
20. shop, store
21. smile, grin
22. burrow, kennel
23. lions, fish
24. puppy, goose
25. assault, attack
26. space, forest
27. game, football
28. encore, repeat
29. December, March
30. church, synagogue
31. frog, newt
32. milkmaid
33. berate
34. angel
35. toadstool
36. wanton
37. store
38. deposit
39. treat
40. type
41. year
42. pals
43. palm
44. real
45. brew
46. D
47. E
48. E
49. D
50. A
51. 6
52. 4
53. 12
54. 24
55. 12
56. 4

57.
M	A	P
O	R	E
B	E	T

(answers may vary as the positioning of the grid can change)

58.
G	A	S
U	G	H
T	O	Y

(answers may vary as the positioning of the grid can change)

59. D
60. due south

Paper 11
1. **e** lung, neigh
2. **o** came, loop
3. **e** case, kite
4. **o** cat, omen *or* **a** cot, mean *or* cot, amen
5. **h** camp, ache *or* **m** chap, mace
6. **e** shin, vane
7. UQEM
8. CVIY
9. IJDNT
10. PLAYER
11. nudge, push
12. sweet, cute
13. realised, attained
14. detrimental, harmful
15. take, steal
16. wolves, whales
17. think, calculate
18. bed, sofa
19. meeting, aid
20. whack, cover
21. hurricane, downpour
22. GAG engaged
23. RAG average
24. CAN hurricane
25. FOR uniform
26. AGE damaged
27. recorder, cello
28. laugh, smile
29. wavy, oblong
30. shadowy, drab
31. tears, lash
32. hopeless
33. singleton
34. reinstate
35. incite
36. reindeer
37. su<u>m</u> <u>m</u>ew, ru<u>m</u> <u>m</u>at
38. rea<u>r</u> <u>r</u>ant, sea<u>r</u> <u>r</u>oar
39. han<u>g</u> <u>g</u>uru, fla<u>g</u> <u>g</u>auge
40. hig<u>h</u> <u>h</u>aul, slus<u>h</u> <u>h</u>eir
41. tugs
42. mews
43. shut
44. sack
45. swan
46. A
47. C
48. B
49. E
50. B
51. D
52. 54
53. 35
54. 36
55. 8
56. 8
57. 5
58. 8
59. E
60. north-west

Paper 12
1. each
2. lies
3. pear
4. veer
5. snow
6. sand
7. **s** area, pops
8. **a** rose, seat
9. **y** band, fury
10. **t** face, bidet
11. **e** fed, theme
12. **t** bough, lasts
13. BUNNY
14. NORTH
15. WHALE
16. BALLOON
17. PQ
18. VX
19. TQ
20. MACHINE
21. RESPONSIBLE
22. SYMPATHETIC
23. INTIMATED
24. REDISTRIBUTE
25. bike, cycle
26. leaves, foliage
27. cook, chef
28. seeks, desires
29. stake, post
30. reign, operate
31. deter, confess
32. party, team
33. burn, douse
34. theatre, cinema
35. penguin, ostrich
36. mature, ancient
37. neighouring, handy
38. tired, bored
39. pea, broad bean
40. earphone
41. simpleton
42. confuse
43. thinnest
44. newton
45. nine
46. vane
47. elms
48. mane
49. none
50. 15
51. 25
52. 54
53. 4
54. 90
55. 6
56. 9
57. 6

58.
O	F	F
D	U	E
E	R	E

(answers may vary as the positioning of the grid can change)

59. Jacob
60. south-east

Work out the code for each question. The alphabet is here to help you.

A B C D E F G H I J K L M N O P Q R S T U V W X Y Z

Example

If the code for DUCK is EVDL, what is the code for SWAN?   _TXBO_

11. If the code for GLOVE is JORYH, what is the code for SCARF?   _____

12. If the code for BEACH is FIEGL, what is the code for OCEAN?   _____

13. If the code for PARTY is TEVXC, what is the code for GIFT?   _____

14. If the code for DRAGON is WIZTLM, what does YVZHG mean?   _____

/4

The pairs of words below are linked in some way. Write, on the answer line provided, the word that completes the second pair, following the same pattern as the first.

Example

GOOSE is to GOOD as MOOSE is to _MOOD_

15. GRIP is to SNIP as GRUFF is to _____

16. CHAIR is to CHAR as STAIR is to _____

17. LEANER is to LEADER as GRUNGE is to _____

18. HEAT is to HATE as LEAN is to _____

/4

Underline the words that are made from the same letters.

Example

NAN   nap   _won_   wow   _now_

19. HEADS   SHEDS   SHADE   DEATH   SHEAR   SPADE

20. TWIST   TWITS   WRIST   SWATS   WAIST   TAWSE

21. METER   TERMS   TEEMS   MEETS   METRE   MATED

/3

39

Underline the **two** words, **one** from each set, that have a **similar meaning**.

Example

(car, take, <u>jump</u>)   (chair, <u>leap</u>, drive)

22. (dinky, puppy, small)   (size, toy, cute)

23. (door, path, exit)   (return, leave, handle)

24. (bus, coach, driver)   (trainer, lorry, guard)

25. (trade, sell, shop)   (counter, items, exchange)

26. (cut, vain, church)   (conceited, blood, vein)

/5

The word in capitals has had a group of three letters taken out. These **three** letters spell another word, without rearranging the order. Write the **three-letter** word on the line provided. The sentence needs to make sense.

Example

I like my bacon cooked very CRI   <u>SPY</u>

27. There are lots of trees in the EST.   _____

28. She's too rough when she TS the page!   _____

29. Does your scarf keep you warm in TER?   _____

30. IR college was badly damaged.   _____

31. The F had died down to embers.   _____

/5

Underline the **two** words, **one** from each set, that when put together, make one new, correctly spelt word. The order of the letters does not change. **The word from the group on the left always comes first.**

Example

(run, <u>use</u>, give)   (take, <u>less</u>, red)

32. (tidy, proper, prim)   (violet, rose, pink)

33. (our, be, hour)   (good, grass, calm)

34. (be, me, so)   (half, hefty, err)

35. (rob, teeth, drink)   (er, bed, her)

36. (mat, sat, bat)   (kind, nave, her)

/5

Find **one** letter that will complete **both** pairs of words, finishing the first word and beginning the second word in each pair. The **same** letter must be used for both pairs of words. Write the letter on the line provided.

Example

pa (t) ap   hi (t) ime

37. coo (_____) ube   wil (_____) our

38. wor (_____) ing   lic (_____) een

39. yet (_____) odine   corg (_____) ota

40. lie (_____) ltra   bayo (_____) sher

/4

In the first set of three words, the middle word has been made from letters in the other two words. Complete the second set of words in the **same** way, to make the missing word, **which must make sense**. Write your answers on the lines provided.

Example

fast (tea) real   leaf (fir) hire

41. post (wet) view   stab (_____) read

42. bean (name) meal   plod (_____) doom

43. near (mane) name   rasp (_____) rats

44. slap (laps) seek   dear (_____) nine

45. teas (safe) flee   near (_____) gene

/5

Letters stand for numbers. Work out the answer to each sum. Write your answer as a **letter** on the line provided.

Example

If A = 2, B = 3, C = 4, D = 5, E = 6, F = 8

what is the answer to this sum written as a letter: D + B = $\underline{F}$

If A = 3, B = 5, C = 6, D = 10, E = 15, what is:

46. (E + D) ÷ B = _____

47. (A × B) – B = _____

48. (B × C) ÷ D = _____

49. (C ÷ A) × B = _____

50. $\dfrac{(C \times E)}{D}$ ÷ A = _____

/5

Write the number that continues each sequence in the most sensible way.

Example

| 3 | 6 | 12 | 21 | 33 | $\underline{48}$ |

51. 5   7   11   19   _____

52. 11   22   34   47   _____

53. 4   11   5   12   6   13   7   _____

54. 22   15   20   17   18   19   16   _____

/4

Find the **relationship** between the **numbers** in the first two sets of brackets. The numbers in the third set of brackets are **related in the same way**. Find the missing number and add it to the final set of brackets.

Example

(6 [48] 8)   (9 [45] 5)   (7 [$\underline{21}$] 3)

55. (8 [6] 2)   (9 [4] 5)   (7 [_____] 4)

56. (9 [20] 11)   (5 [13] 8)   (6 [_____] 9)

57. (3 [15] 5)   (2 [16] 8)   (5 [_____] 5)

/3

Write the words into the grid so they can be read across or down.

Example

YET   EYE   WET   MEW   AYE   MAY

58. PAD   NEW   ARE   PEN   DEW   ERE

/1

59. Mick, Sharon, Ralph, Jason and Paige are all proud members of the school orchestra.

Mick and Ralph play the oboe.

Four of the five children play the recorder.

Sharon and Paige play the violin.

Jason and Paige play the tambourine.

Mick and Jason also play the cello, but Jason can't play the recorder.

Who plays the tambourine, violin and recorder? _____

/1

60. The hospital is due north of the football stadium and due west of Maurice's house.

The bus station is south-east of the hospital.

Maurice's house is due north of the bus station.

These four places form the points of a square.

Where is Maurice's house in relation to the football stadium? _____

/1

/60

PAPER 8

In the following sentences, a word of **four letters** is hidden across the **end** of one word and the **start** of the next word. Write the hidden word on the line provided. The letter order **cannot** be changed.

Example

The shop was la**st op**en on Tuesday.   *stop*

1. She uses ink whereas I prefer pencil.   _____

2. Watching friends eating always makes me hungry.   _____

3. Can you give me details of all the categories and sections please?   _____

4. I have seen a busker dance for money on the street.   _____

5. He turned up the oven to make sure his food was well cooked.   _____

/5

Change the first word of the third pair in the same way as the other pairs to give a new word. Write the answer on the line provided.

Example

tray, dray   tram, dram   trip, <u>drip</u>

6. slim, mile   slip, pile   grit, _____

7. made, dame   tame, mate   sore, _____

8. time, emit   plug, gulp   reed, _____

9. stain, stair   pain, pair   lain, _____

/4

Underline the word that **can** be made from the letters of the word in capitals.

Example

CRUSADER   <u>crude</u>   rush   pears   raider   dress

10. ABSENTED   dear   dented   teased   tasered   beaters

11. BROCHURE   cured   chores   brooch   reach   cherub

12. COAGENTS   tongues   octanes   count   octagon   stench

/3

> Underline the **two** words, **one** from each set, that will complete each sentence in the most sensible way.

Example

Head is to (face, arm, <u>neck</u>) as foot is to (<u>leg</u>, knee, thigh).

13. Girl is to (person, play, boy) as woman is to (man, teacher, adult).

14. Leopard is to (spots, animal, cat) as zebra is to (stars, lines, stripes).

15. Smart is to (intelligent, sting, hurt) as sly is to (dishonest, dumb, sneaky).

16. Weight is to (diet, heavy, grams) as height is to (wide, metres, length).

17. Soft is to (harsh, brittle, breeze) as spectator is to (wind, crowd, participant).

/5

> The word in capitals has had a group of three letters taken out. These **three** letters spell another word, without rearranging the order. Write the **three-letter** word on the line provided. The sentence needs to make sense.

Example

I like my bacon cooked very CRI   <u>SPY</u>

18. I'm sorry I was late, but my train was DEED.   _____

19. The hills are covered with purple HHER.   _____

20. It's too hot for long TRORS.   _____

21. It wasn't such a GD idea, after all.   _____

22. I can't afford LEAT!   _____

/5

> Underline the **two** words in each group that are **different** from the others.

Example

<u>potato</u>   lemon   banana   <u>cabbage</u>   strawberry

23. cotton   wool   wood   glass   metal

24. violin   guitar   harp   oboe   drum

25. danger   bell   whistle   siren   concern

26. raspberry   apple   strawberry   orange   banana

27. toaster   scales   bath   fridge   cooker

/5

Underline the **two** words, **one** from each set, that when put together, make one new correctly spelt word. The order of the letters does not change. **The word from the group on the left always comes first.**

Example

(run, <u>use</u>, give)   (take, <u>less</u>, red)

28. (grass, field, farm)   (cow, hen, yard)

29. (speed, come, in)   (go, sect, fact)

30. (bet, bat, bun)   (he, lass, she)

31. (so, be, please)   (red, ached, ant)

32. (work, tact, an)   (ticks, tics, hard)

/5

Underline **one** word from the list in brackets that goes equally well with both pairs of words outside the brackets.

Example

(ribbon, <u>present</u>, play, theatre, party)

gift, token   show, demonstrate

33. (pop, ribbon, football, group, organise)

    team, band   arrange, categorise

34. (tell, page, book, keep, safeguard)

    story, magazine   arrest, reserve

35. (door, smash, contemplate, frame, reflect)

    mirror, glass   think, consider

36. (book, page, word, call, alert)

    newspaper, journal   notify, summon

/4

In the first set of three words, the middle word has been made from letters in the other two words. Complete the second set of words in the **same** way, to make the missing word, **which must make sense**. Write your answers on the lines provided.

Example

fast (tea) real   leaf ($\underline{fir}$) hire

37. send (now) flow   kind (_____) chew

38. head (mead) dame   rake (_____) rare

39. peer (earn) rain   ride (_____) nine

40. slap (laps) seek   dear (_____) need

41. teas (safe) flee   near (_____) rage

/5

Letters stand for numbers. Work out the answer to each sum. Write your answer as a **letter** on the line provided.

Example

If $A = 2, B = 3, C = 4, D = 5, E = 6, F = 8$

what is the answer to this sum written as a letter: $D + B = \underline{F}$

If $A = 2, B = 3, C = 4, D = 8, E = 10, F = 12$, what is:

42. $(C \times F) \div F = $ _____

43. $(B \times C) - A = $ _____

44. $\dfrac{(C \times D) - A}{E} = $ _____

45. $(F \div B) + C = $ _____

46. $(B \times D) \div A = $ _____

47. $\dfrac{A + D + E}{D + A} = $ _____

/6

Find the missing **pair of letters** in the series.
The alphabet is provided to help you.

A B C D E F G H I J K L M N O P Q R S T U V W X Y Z

Example

MO   MK   OQ   KI   *QS*

48. KX   JV   IT   HR   GP   FN   _____

49. UR   PM   KH   FC   AX   _____

50. NO   NM   OP   ML   PQ   LK   _____

51. MN   OL   KP   QJ   IR   SH   _____

52. MO   KQ   IS   GU   EW   CY   _____

/5

Write the number that continues each sequence in the most sensible way.

Example

3   6   12   21   33   *48*

53. 38   26   35   29   32   32   _____

54. 15   5   20   10   30   20   50   40   _____

55. 23   33   24   32   25   31   _____

56. 88   104   44   52   22   26   11   _____

/4

To complete these questions, **balance the numbers** on each side of the
equation. Start by working out the calculation on the left. Next, find the
missing number that will give the **same total** on the right-hand side.

Example

$10 \times 6 \div 5 = 22 + 3 - [\,13\,]$

57. $(8 + 4) - 10 = (6 + 3) -$ _____

58. $(4 \times 6) \div 2 = 18 + 7 -$ _____

/2

59. Charlotte, Matthew and Chrissy all have to be in bed by 9pm on a school night. Matthew gets tired easily and is always in bed by 8.50pm. On Thursday night, Chrissy's bus home from Guides broke down and she didn't arrive home till 9.15pm.

Which of the following statements is true?

A) Charlotte sometimes goes to bed late.

B) Chrissy is never in bed on time.

C) Matthew is never late for bed on a school night.

D) Chrissy is sometimes in bed by 8.30pm.

E) Matthew sometimes misses his bus home. _____   /1

60. The duck pond is due west of Jean's salon and north west of the taxi rank.

The taxi rank is due south of Jean's salon.

The florists' is due west of the taxi rank.

These four places form the points of a square.

Where is the florists' in relation to Jean's salon? _____   /1

/60

PAPER 9

These **four** words have been written as **number codes**, but one of the codes is missing. The words and codes are not necessarily in the same order. Write the answers to the questions on the lines provided.

GIRTH   GISTS   GIRLS   GRIPE

72545   72348   72395

1. Pick out the code for GISTS   _____

2. Pick out the word with the number code 72395   _____

3. Pick out the code for GIRTH   _____

4. What is the code for SHIRT?   _____   /4

Move **one** letter from the first word and add it to the second word to make two new words. Do **not** rearrange any other letters. Write **both** new words, which **must make sense**, on the lines provided.

Example

table   read   →   _able_   _tread_

5. plays   end   →   _____   _____

6. skid   see   →   _____   _____

7. spike   pin   →   _____   _____

8. breathe   tub   →   _____   _____

9. deify   wave   →   _____   _____

10. axle   camp   →   _____   _____   /6

Work out the code for each question. The alphabet is here to help you.

A B C D E F G H I J K L M N O P Q R S T U V W X Y Z

Example

If the code for DUCK is EVDL, what is the code for SWAN?   _TXBO_

11. If the code for CARVE is ECTXG, what is the code for SLICE?   _____

12. If the code for COAST is EQCUV, what is the code for OCEAN?   _____

13. If the code for RIVER is OFSBO, what does IXHB mean?   _____

14. If the code for KITE is PRGV, what does GZRO mean?   _____   /4

Find the pair of letters that completes the sentence in the most sensible way. The alphabet has been printed below to help you.

> A B C D E F G H I J K L M N O P Q R S T U V W X Y Z

Example

BY is to EV as HS is to _KP_

15. CF is to GJ as RU is to _____

16. FA is to BH as OJ is to _____

17. MI is to NR as GC is to _____

18. HF is to SU as KI is to _____

/4

Underline the **two** words, **one** from each set, that have a **similar meaning**.

Example

(car, take, <u>jump</u>)   (chair, <u>leap</u>, drive)

19. (quit, walk, quiet)   (quite, leave, run)

20. (winch, letter, docks)   (lift, rope, wire)

21. (way, compass, place)   (pole, cold, direction)

22. (cover, paste, walking)   (stick, decorate, paper)

23. (sum, government, prime)   (number, minister, main)

/5

Underline the **two** words, **one** from each set, that will complete each sentence in the most sensible way.

Example

Head is to (face, arm, <u>neck</u>) as foot is to (<u>leg</u>, knee, thigh).

24. Sock is to (foot, toe, hit) as glove is to (knock, wear, hand).

25. Child is to (young, baby, human) as kitten is to (basket, cat, old).

26. Reject is to (discard, accept, extra) as disappoint is to (regret, fail, impress).

27. Desert is to (cactus, habitat, sand) as crossword is to (puzzle, newspaper, rainforest).

28. Swarm is to (gather, summer, bees) as herd is to (listened, cattle, wasps).

/5

The word in capitals has had a group of three letters taken out. These **three** letters spell another word, without rearranging the order. Write the **three-letter** word on the line provided. The sentence needs to make sense.

Example

I like my bacon cooked very CRI _SPY_

29. The CO blazed a trail through space. _____

30. She missed the LY bus. _____

31. I used a towel to stop me getting too SWY. _____

32. I don't own a G ring. _____

33. Look at the ST of you! _____

/5

Find **one** letter that will complete **both** pairs of words, finishing the first word and beginning the second word in each pair. The **same** letter must be used for both pairs of words. Write the letter on the line provided.

Example

pa (t) ap   hi (t) ime

34. bre _____ am   bar _____ uos

35. dea _____ uel   clif _____ ool

36. tho _____ rban   burea _____ surp

37. catc _____ url   tras _____ airy

/4

In the first set of three words, the middle word has been made from letters in the other two words. Complete the second set of words in the **same** way, to make the missing word, **which must make sense**. Write your answers on the lines provided.

Example

fast (tea) real   leaf (fir) hire

38. page (rap) turn   dale (_____) best

39. pony (open) lone   etch (_____) pane

40. hems (elms) cell   slid (_____) navy

41. unit (shut) hues   neat (_____) idol

42. call (palm) camp   main (_____) warp

/5

Find the missing **pair of letters** in the series. The alphabet is provided to help you.

A B C D E F G H I J K L M N O P Q R S T U V W X Y Z

Example

AD   CF   EH   GJ   IL   KN

43. _____   YB   XC   WD   VE   _____

44. _____   BS   CO   DK   EG   _____

45. _____   YH   XL   WP   VT   _____

46. _____   CF   EH   GJ   _____   KN

47. _____   _____   VS   TQ   RO   PM

/5

Find the **relationship** between the **numbers** in the first two sets of brackets. The numbers in the third set of brackets are **related in the same way**. Find the missing number and add it to the final set of brackets.

Example

(6 [48] 8)   (9 [45] 5)   (7 [21] 3)

48. (5 [14] 9)   (8 [18] 10)   (6 [_____] 13)

49. (6 [30] 5)   (8 [32] 4)   (9 [_____] 6)

50. (36 [3] 3)   (144 [9] 3)   (121 [_____] 3)

To complete these questions, **balance the numbers** on each side of the equation. Start by working out the calculation on the left. Next, find the missing number that will give the **same total** on the right-hand side.

Example

$10 \times 6 \div 5 = 22 + 3 - [\,13\,]$

51. $(2 \times 8) \div 4 = 7 - 6 +$ _____

52. $(8 \times 5) \div 4 = 22 - 8 -$ _____

Change the first word of the third pair in the same way as the other pairs to give a new word. Write the answer on the line provided.

Example

tray, dray   tram, dram   trip, <u>drip</u>

53. time, emit   plug, gulp   reed, _____

54. hurdle, hurdling   cycle, cycling   dive, _____

55. notion, not   dangerous, danger   ghoulish, _____

56. slim, mile   grit, tire   plum, _____

57. mare, ream   tame, meat   moat, _____

Write the words into the grid so they can be read across or down.

Example

YET   EYE   WET   MEW   AYE   MAY

58. ANY   TOD   ONE   TAP   DYE   PEE

/1

59. Carl, Kevin, Natasha, Kelly and Sunil have all been abroad.

Four of the five children have been to France.

Kevin has been to France and Spain.

Carl and Natasha have been to Greece and Sunil and Carl have been to Germany.

Sunil has also visited Egypt. Kelly has been to Spain and Egypt but not France.

Which child has been to France, Greece and Germany? _____ /1

60. The car park is due west of the hotel and north-west of the statue.

The statue is due east of Bryan's Bar.

The hotel is due north of the statue.

These four places form the points of a square.

Where is Bryan's Bar in relation to the hotel? _____ /1

/60

PAPER 10

In the following sentences, a word of **four letters** is hidden across the **end** of one word and the **start** of the next word. Write the hidden word on the line provided. The letter order **cannot** be changed.

Example

The shop was la**st op**en on Tuesday. _stop_

1. I know that all the rain has dried up. _____

2. I like to scoff individual pieces of pie! _____

3. My conference speech earned me a round of applause! _____

4. How water-tight is that urn? _____

5. He employed a new henchman. _____

6. I got it right hence I understood. _____

/6

Work out the code for each question. The alphabet is here to help you.

A B C D E F G H I J K L M N O P Q R S T U V W X Y Z

Example

If the code for DUCK is EVDL, what is the code for SWAN?   _TXBO_

7. If the code for DOG is BME, what is the code for CAT? _____

8. If the code for LUCKY is QZHPD, what is the code for CHANCE? _____

9. If the code for SPICE is XUNHJ, what is the code for FOOD? _____

10. If the code for NEPTUNE is MCMPPHX what does DYOPC mean? _____

/4

The pairs of words below are linked in some way. Write, on the answer line provided, the word that completes the second pair, following the same pattern as the first.

Example

GOOSE is to GOOD as MOOSE is to _MOOD_

11. TOIL is to FOIL as TAKE is to _____

12. SLASH is to SLAMMING as SWISH is to _____

13. TERRACE is to TRACE as BERETS is to _____

14. BARD is to BEARD as HARD is to _____

/4

Underline the word that **can** be made from the letters of the word in capitals.

Example

CRUSADER   <u>crude</u>   rush   pears   raider   dress

15. ACCREDIT   decent   tires   editor   direct   cradle

16. CREAKILY   eclair   croaky   aerial   layers   locker

/2

Underline the **two** words, **one** from each set, that have a **similar meaning**.

Example

(car, take, <u>jump</u>)   (chair, <u>leap</u>, drive)

17. (breathe, nose, smell)   (nice, pleasant, odour)

18. (hospital, sick, help)   (ill, doctor, injury)

19. (wind, storm, blow)   (weave, twist, cold)

20. (shop, buy, purchase)   (goods, street, store)

21. (wink, eyes, smile)   (teeth, lips, grin)

/5

Underline the **two** words, **one** from each set, that will complete each sentence in the most sensible way.

Example

Head is to (face, arm, <u>neck</u>) as foot is to (<u>leg</u>, knee, thigh).

22. Rabbit is to (teeth, burrow, ears) as dog is to (dig, jaws, kennel).

23. Pride is to (proud, lions, modest) as shoal is to (fish, shawl, happy).

24. Litter is to (puppy, mess, bin) as gaggle is to (gander, farm, goose).

25. Battery is to (electricity, assault, torch) as strike is to (attack, match, light).

26. Comet is to (shop, space, ocean) as bird is to (forest, lake, star).

/5

Underline the **two** words in each group that are **different** from the others.

Example

<u>potato</u>   lemon   banana   <u>cabbage</u>   strawberry

27. kick   throw   game   score   football

28. original   encore   first   repeat   initial

29. December   March   April   November   June

30. church   vicar   priest   synagogue   rabbi

31. shark   frog   seal   jellyfish   newt

/5

Underline the **two** words, **one** from each set, that when put together, make one new, correctly spelt word. The order of the letters does not change. **The word from the group on the left always comes first.**

Example

(run, <u>use</u>, give)   (take, <u>less</u>, red)

32. (milk, cow, grass)   (drink, maid, made)

33. (going, be, now)   (go, rate, less)

34. (ant, rip, an)   (tea, gel, tear)

35. (barn, toad, hunch)   (down, mine, stool)

36. (fur, want, lent)   (some, any, on)

/5

Underline **one** word from the list in brackets that goes equally well with both pairs of words outside the brackets.

Example

(ribbon, <u>present</u>, play, theatre, party)

gift, token   show, demonstrate

37. (away, store, mortgage, buy, purchase)

    shop, boutique   deposit, stow

38. (cash, purchase, deposit, leave, situation)

money, funds   put, place

39. (impress, riches, treat, look, knob)

luxury, delight   regard, handle

40. (generous, organise, paper, type, draw)

sort, kind   write, script

/4

In the first set of three words, the middle word has been made from letters in the other two words. Complete the second set of words in the **same** way, to make the missing word, **which must make sense**. Write your answers on the lines provided.

Example

fast (tea) real   leaf (fir) hire

41. eels (owls) down   star (_____) eyed

42. swam (mews) stem   clip (_____) swab

43. warp (pair) main   camp (_____) call

44. diet (tied) died   near (_____) lean

45. ways (wart) tray   beer (_____) were

/5

Letters stand for numbers. Work out the answer to each sum. Write your answer as a **letter** on the line provided.

Example

If $A = 2, B = 3, C = 4, D = 5, E = 6, F = 8$

what is the answer to this sum written as a letter: $D + B = \underline{F}$

If $A = 2, B = 8, C = 12, D = 20, E = 40$, what is:

46. $\dfrac{A \times (B + C)}{A} = $ _____

47. $A \times (A + B) + E - D = $ _____

48. $A \times (A + B) + D = $ _____

49. $\dfrac{C + B + D}{A} =$ _____

50. $\dfrac{D + B + C}{D} =$ _____

/5

Find the **relationship** between the **numbers** in the first two sets of brackets. The numbers in the third set of brackets are **related in the same way**. Find the missing number and add it to the final set of brackets.

Example

(6 [48] 8)   (9 [45] 5)   (7 [21] 3)

51. (64 [4] 4)   (81 [4] 5)   (100 [_____] 4)

52. (24 [4] 6)   (18 [9] 2)   (28 [_____] 7)

53. (21 [3] 7)   (36 [4] 9)   (48 [_____] 4)

/3

To complete these questions, **balance the numbers** on each side of the equation. Start by working out the calculation on the left. Next, find the missing number that will give the **same total** on the right-hand side.

Example

$10 \times 6 \div 5 = 22 + 3 - [13]$

54. $(18 \times 5) \div 3 = 18 + 36 -$ _____

55. $\dfrac{17 - 3}{7} = 4 \times \dfrac{(2 \times 3)}{\rule{2em}{0.4pt}}$

56. $\dfrac{31 + 9}{5} =$ _____ $\times \dfrac{(18 + 2)}{10}$

/3

Write the words into the grid so they can be read across or down.

Example

YET   EYE   WET   MEW   AYE   MAY

M	A	Y
E	Y	E
W	E	T

57. ARE   PET   ORE   MAP   BET   MOB

58. AGO   GUT   GAS   UGH   TOY   SHY

/2

59. Sadie, Phil, Shofiq, Bill and Sean all have Saturday jobs.

Sadie and Sean earn the same amount as each other; £4 less than Bill.

Shofiq earns £2 more than Sadie and Sean.

Phil earns the least, exactly half of Bill.

Bill earns the highest amount of everyone, £10.

Which one of the following statements is true:

A) Sean and Shofiq earn the same amount.

B) Phil earns £6.

C) Sadie and Sean work together.

D) Shofiq earns £8.

E) Together Sean and Sadie earn £14 _____

/1

60. The caves are north-east of Tony's Marina and due east of the lighthouse.

The monument is due east of Tony's Marina.

The lighthouse is north-west of the monument.

These four places form the points of a square.

Where is Tony's Marina in relation to the lighthouse? _____

/1

/60

PAPER 11

Move **one** letter from the first word and add it to the second word to make two new words. Do **not** rearrange any other letters. Write **both** new words, which **must make sense**, on the lines provided.

Example

table   reed   →   _tale_   _breed_

1. lunge   nigh   →   _____   _____

2. cameo   lop   →   _____   _____

3. cease   kit   →   _____   _____

4. coat   men   →   _____   _____

5. champ   ace   →   _____   _____

6. shine   van   →   _____   _____

/6

Work out the code for each question. The alphabet is here to help you.

A B C D E F G H I J K L M N O P Q R S T U V W X Y Z

Example

If the code for DUCK is EVDL, what is the code for SWAN?   _TXBO_

7. If the code for SHOE is UJQG, what is the code for SOCK?   _____

8. If the code for WRIST is RMDNO, what is the code for HAND?   _____

9. If the code for BANGS is WVIBN, what is the code for NOISY?   _____

10. If the code for GUITAR is LZNYFW, what does UQFDJW mean?   _____

/4

Underline the **two** words, **one** from each set, that have a **similar meaning**.

Example

(car, take, <u>jump</u>)   (chair, <u>leap</u>, drive)

11. (nudge, walk, position)   (push, enter, drop)

12. (sweet, lump, taste)   (sugar, cute, culture)

13. (realised, obtained, knew)   (old, scored, attained)

14. (weak, sore, detrimental)   (harmful, slippery, pleasant)

15. (metal, take, twig)   (steal, wood, heavy)

/5

Underline the **two** words, **one** from each set, that will complete each sentence in the most sensible way.

Example

Head is to (face, arm, <u>neck</u>) as foot is to (<u>leg</u>, knee, thigh).

16. Pack is to (holiday, wolves, suitcase) as school is to (classroom, whales, assembly).

17. Reason is to (think, dream, plan) as add is to (subtract, calculate, nightmare).

18. Pillow is to (bed, cloud, night) as cushion is to (sofa, pin, feather).

19. Summit is to (height, tower, meeting) as help is to (aid, police, accident).

20. Hammer is to (tool, whack, box) as plaster is to (cover, gash, blood).

21. Windy is to (hurricane, polar, bend) as wet is to (cold, raincoat, downpour).

/6

The word in capitals has had a group of three letters taken out. These **three** letters spell another word, without rearranging the order. Write the **three-letter** word on the line provided. The sentence needs to make sense.

Example

I like my bacon cooked very CRI   <u>SPY</u>

22. The couple were married soon after getting ENED.   _____

23. For him, his performance was only AVEE.   _____

24. We were all evacuated because of the HURRIE. _____

25. Polish the buttons on your UNIM. _____

26. Take back those DAMD ones. _____

/5

Underline the **two** words in each group that are **different** from the others.

Example

<u>potato</u>   lemon   banana   <u>cabbage</u>   strawberry

27. bongo   recorder   tambourine   triangle   cello

28. bite   laugh   eat   smile   chew

29. wavy   cylindrical   spherical   oblong   rotund

30. shining   shadowy   glaring   drab   radiant

31. tears   wink   cry   squint   lash

/5

Underline the **two** words, **one** from each set, that when put together, make one new, correctly spelt word. The order of the letters does not change. **The word from the group on the left always comes first.**

Example

(run, <u>use</u>, give)   (take, <u>less</u>, red)

32. (give, hope, take)   (less, more, some)

33. (way, single, double)   (tonne, ton, one)

34. (rain, rein, ran)   (splash, float, state)

35. (on, in, at)   (cite, ten, ton)

36. (reign, rein, up)   (coat, deer, shower)

/5

Find **one** letter that will complete **both** pairs of words, finishing the first word and beginning the second word in each pair. The **same** letter must be used for both pairs of words. Write the letter on the line provided.

Example

pa (t) ap   hi (t) ime

37. su _____ ew   ru _____ at

38. rea _____ ant   sea _____ oar

39. han _____ uru   fla _____ auge

40. hig _____ aul   slus _____ eir

/4

In the first set of three words, the middle word has been made from letters in the other two words. Complete the second set of words in the **same** way, to make the missing word, **which must make sense**. Write your answers on the lines provided.

Example

fast (tea) real   leaf (fir) hire

41. fats (said) lied   quit (_____) ages

42. swab (pals) clip   stem (_____) swam

43. idol (lint) neat   hues (_____) unit

44. sawn (swan) plan   scar (_____) teak

45. teak (sack) scar   plan (_____) sawn

/5

Letters stand for numbers. Work out the answer to each sum. Write your answer as a **letter** on the line provided.

Example

If A = 2, B = 3, C = 4, D = 5, E = 6, F = 8

what is the answer to this sum written as a letter: D + B = <u>F</u>

If A = 3, B = 8, C = 9, D = 24, E = 72, what is:

46. $\dfrac{A \times (A \times B)}{D}$ = _____

47. $\dfrac{A \times (B \times A)}{B}$ = _____

48. $\dfrac{A \times (B \times A)}{C}$ = _____

49. A × (D + B – C) + A = _____

50. $\dfrac{C \times (D \div A)}{A \times A}$ = _____

51. $\dfrac{(A \times C \times A) - C}{A}$ = _____

/6

Write the number that continues each sequence in the most sensible way.

Example

3   6   12   21   33   <u>48</u>

52. 21   48   22   49   24   51   27   _____

53. 63   11   59   15   51   23   39   _____

54. 97   18   94   21   88   27   79   _____

55. 12   13   11   14   10   15   9   16   _____

/4

To complete these questions, **balance the numbers** on each side of the equation. Start by working out the calculation on the left. Next, find the missing number that will give the **same total** on the right-hand side.

Example

$10 \times 6 \div 5 = 22 + 3 - [\ \underline{13}\ ]$

56. $(18 - 7) - 6 = (9 - \underline{\hspace{2em}}) + 4$

57. $\dfrac{31 - 4}{3} = \dfrac{3 \times (5 \times 3)}{\underline{\hspace{2em}}}$

58. $\dfrac{21 + 11}{2} = \underline{\hspace{2em}} \times \dfrac{(9 \times 4)}{18}$

/3

59. Pauline, Ronnie, Tyrone and Mitch all need to score 90% on their spelling test to get through to the county finals.

Mitch scored 83%.

Both Tyrone and Pauline scored higher than Mitch, but Ronnie beat everyone with a score of 96%.

Which one of the following statements is true?

A) Pauline got through to the county finals.

B) Tyrone didn't get through to the county finals.

C) Both Pauline and Tyrone did get through to the county finals.

D) Mitch will enter next year's competition.

E) Ronnie was successful this year. _____

/1

60. Edna's butcher's shop is due west of the fruit shop and due north of the fire station.

The fire station is due west of the Community Centre.

The fruit shop is north-east of the fire station.

These four places form the points of a square.

Where is Edna's butcher's shop in relation to the Community Centre? _____

/1

/60

PAPER 12

In the following sentences, a word of **four letters** is hidden across the **end** of one word and the **start** of the next word. Write the hidden word on the line provided. The letter order **cannot** be changed.

Example

The shop was la**st op**en on Tuesday. <u>stop</u>

1. The cold sea chilled him to the bone. _____

2. Lie still, you're making me nervous! _____

3. It's going to be damp early tomorrow morning. _____

4. The accident was due to a valve error. _____

5. It is now or never! _____

6. Take deep breaths and relax. _____

/6

Move **one** letter from the first word and add it to the second word to make two new words. Do **not** rearrange any other letters. Write **both** new words, which **must make sense**, on the lines provided.

Example

table   reed   →   <u>tale</u>   <u>breed</u>

7. areas   pop   →   _____   _____

8. arose   set   →   _____   _____

9. bandy   fur   →   _____   _____

10. facet   bide   →   _____   _____

11. feed   them   →   _____   _____

12. bought   lass   →   _____   _____

/6

Work out the code for each question. The alphabet is here to help you.

A B C D E F G H I J K L M N O P Q R S T U V W X Y Z

Example

If the code for DUCK is EVDL, what is the code for SWAN? _TXBO_

13. If the code for EASTER is HDVWHU, what does EXQQB mean? _____

14. If the code for SAFETY is WEJIXC, what does RSVXL mean? _____

15. If the code for SHARK is RFXNF, what does VFXHZ mean? _____

16. If the code for EXPLODE is IBTPSHI, what does FEPPSSR mean? _____   /4

Find the pair of letters that completes the sentence in the most sensible way. The alphabet has been printed below to help you.

A B C D E F G H I J K L M N O P Q R S T U V W X Y Z

Example

BY is to EV as HS is to _KP_

17. DE is to FG as NO is to _____

18. DB is to WY as EC is to _____

19. GH is to IF as RS is to _____   /3

Rearrange **all** the capital letters to form a correctly spelt word that will complete the sentences sensibly. Write the word on the answer line.

Example

His pet rabbit was hungry so he fed him a juicy TOCARR. _CARROT_

20. Has the washing CHAMEIN leaked all over the floor? _____

21. Because you are so SBOSENPRIEL, you can be form captain! _____

22. Everyone was so understanding and MYSETTAPHIC about
my accident. _____

23. It was never stated, just DIMATEINT. _____

24. Help me BURERIDSITTE this money to the needy! _____

/5

Underline the **two** words, **one** from each set, that have a **similar meaning**.

Example

(car, take, <u>jump</u>)   (chair, <u>leap</u>, drive)

25. (car, bike, rider)   (walk, path, cycle)

26. (leaves, goes, shoots)   (plants, foliage, gun)

27. (restaurant, feed, cook)   (kitchen, waiter, chef)

28. (turban, seeks, church)   (root, religious, desires)

29. (stake, letter, greet)   (beef, meat, post)

/5

Underline the **two** words, **one** from each set, that will
complete each sentence in the most sensible way.

Example

Head is to (face, arm, <u>neck</u>) as foot is to (<u>leg</u>, knee, thigh).

30. King is to (queen, ruler, reign) as surgeon is to (hospital, operate, patient).

31. Discourage is to (deter, stop, ban) as confide is to (agree, allow, confess).

32. Host is to (organise, arrange, party) as captain is to (orchestra, team, chief).

33. Torch is to (burn, bulb, battery) as extinguish is to (off, fire, douse).

34. Play is to (television, theatre, game) as film is to (actor, cinema, usher).

/5

Underline the **two** words in each group that are **different** from the others.

Example

<u>potato</u>   lemon   banana   <u>cabbage</u>   strawberry

35. penguin   owl   ostrich   pigeon   parrot

36. mature   adolescent   ancient   young   juvenile

37. out-lying   remote   distant   neighbouring   handy

38. excited   interested   tired   bored   fascinated

39. leek   potato   pea   broad bean   carrot

/5

Underline the **two** words, **one** from each set, that when put together, make one new, correctly spelt word. The order of the letters does not change. **The word from the group on the left always comes first.**

Example

(run, <u>use</u>, give)   (take, <u>less</u>, red)

40. (ear, nose, eye)   (say, phone, talk)

41. (act, met, simple)   (tonne, tor, ton)

42. (sink, con, no)   (fuse, bed, down)

43. (thin, fur, fat)   (there, nest, herd)

44. (high, new, old)   (place, hill, ton)

/5

In the first set of three words, the middle word has been made from letters in the other two words. Complete the second set of words in the **same** way, to make the missing word, **which must make sense**. Write your answers on the lines provided.

Example

fast (tea) real   leaf (<u>fir</u>) hire

45. crab (rate) tend   snip (_____) news

46. snib (nice) celt   oval (_____) next

47. navy (avid) slid　　cell (_____) hems

48. rats (tars) rasp　　name (_____) near

49. pool (poor) oral　　noon (_____) neon

/5

Find the **relationship** between the **numbers** in the first two sets of brackets. The numbers in the third set of brackets are **related in the same way**. Find the missing number and add it to the final set of brackets.

Example

(6 [48] 8)　　(9 [45] 5)　　(7 [21] 3)

50. (9 [20] 11)　　(5 [13] 8)　　(6 [_____] 9)

51. (3 [15] 5)　　(2 [16] 8)　　(5 [_____] 5)

52. (6 [30] 5)　　(8 [32] 4)　　(9 [_____] 6)

53. (24 [4] 6)　　(18 [9] 2)　　(28 [_____] 7)

54. (7 [56] 7)　　(8 [72] 8)　　(9 [_____] 9)

55. (49 [8] 1)　　(81 [10] 1)　　(25 [_____] 1)

/6

To complete these questions, **balance the numbers** on each side of the equation. Start by working out the calculation on the left. Next, find the missing number that will give the **same total** on the right-hand side.

Example

$10 \times 6 \div 5 = 22 + 3 - [13]$

56. $\dfrac{(7 + 3) - 2}{2} = 12 - \left(\dfrac{}{3}\right) - 5$

57. $\dfrac{7 + 17}{4} = 2 \times \left(\dfrac{6 \times 3}{}\right)$

/2

Write the words into the grid so they can be read across or down.

Example

YET   EYE   WET   MEW   AYE   MAY

58. ODE   FUR   ERE   DUE   FEE   OFF

/1

59. Five children, Samir, Jacob, Selma, Kevin and Ruby are all proud members of their school book club.

Samir, Selma and Kevin like adventure stories and funny stories.

Ruby likes ghost stories, school stories and adventure stories.

Jacob likes school stories, funny stories and ghost stories.

Who doesn't like adventure stories? _____

/1

60. Syd's Chippie is due north of the adventure playground and north-east of the tip.

The beach is due west of Syd's Chippie.

The adventure playground is due east of the tip.

These four places form the points of a square.

Where is the adventure playground in relation to the beach? _____

/1

/60

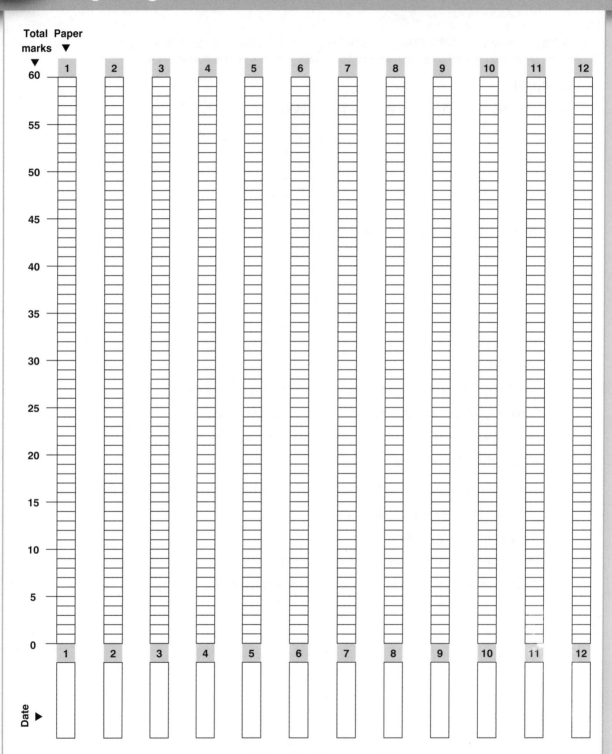

Total Paper
marks ▼
▼
60

55

50

45

40

35

30

25

20

15

10

5

0

1 2 3 4 5 6 7 8 9 10 11 12

Date ▶

Now colour in your score!